# Contents

## Seek and Find

Can you find these objects in your book?

page 24

page 13

page 19

page 7

page 15

page 22

Solving Hidden Pictures puzzles develops figure-ground perception and improves the ability to establish object constancy and size relationships. Educators have shown that working on these puzzles can enhance a child's attention to detail, reinforce good work habits, increase word knowledge, and aid in developing self-confidence.

hot dog

pig

rug

flag

bag

jug

frog

mug

egg

plug

Illustrated by Valeri Gorbachev

**Try to write some of your favorite words that have g at the end of their names on the lines below.**

dog

Can you find the 10 objects hidden in the picture that have the letter g at the end of their names? Answers on page 30

3

**These 8 funny things are happening in the scene.**
**Can you find them all?** Answers on page 30

# Imagine and Draw

**What is the silliest thing you might see in the bathtub?**
**Draw a picture of it here.** ▮▮ CRAYON ▮▮

Illustrated by Nathan Jarvis

Lauren and her family like to dig for clams at low tide. Tonight her dad will make steamed clams for supper.

**Can you find these hidden objects on the next page?**

Answers on page 30

lollipop

slice of pizza

rocket ship

socks

sheep

ice-cream cone

book

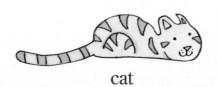

cat

**Can you guess the answer to each riddle? Use the Hidden Pictures® words if you need help.**

I always wear a woolly coat.

And when you cannot sleep,

Just count me one by one each night

Because I am a _____.

If you want to see the stars,

I'll take you on a trip.

Climb inside and we'll blast off.

I am a _____.

People say I have nine lives.

Now why would they say that?

I like to purr and take long naps.

Did you guess that I'm a _____?

I'm handy when your feet are cold

And when you go for walks.

I keep your "piggies" nice and warm.

I am a pair of _____.

Illustrated by Jamie Smith

Can you find the Hidden Pictures below? When you finish, you can color in the

# Game of Tag



rest of the scene. CRAYON Answers on page 30 Illustrated by Susan T. Hall

**Can you find 10 eggs on the next page?** Answers on page 31

Color in an egg in this box each time you find an egg in the picture.

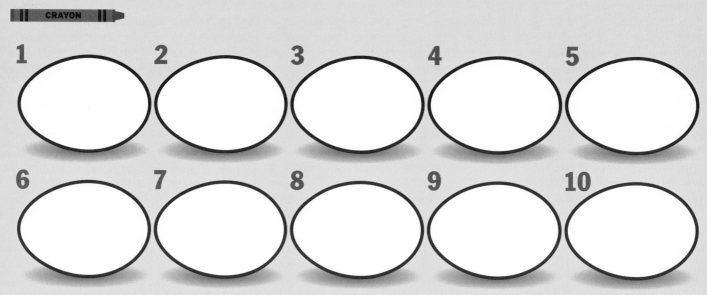

CRAYON

1 2 3 4 5

6 7 8 9 10

Connect the dots from ① to ㉚. When you finish, you will see something that hatches from an egg.

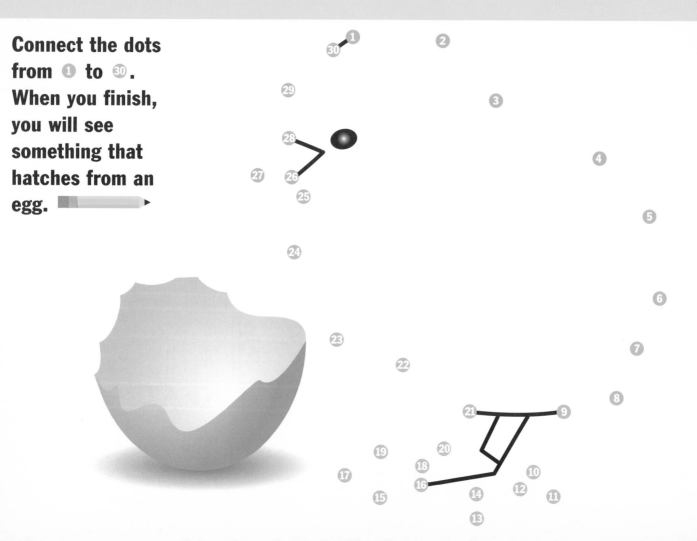

Ethan and his friends practice their tricks
on his skateboard ramp.

**Can you find 8 Hidden Pictures® on the next page?** Answers on page 31

paper airplane

nail

ruler

umbrella

ladle

envelope

bowl

rocket ship

Illustrated by Ron Lieser

**Color in each shape that has an orange dot with an orange crayon.** ‖ CRAYON ‖
**Color in each shape that has a black dot with a black crayon.** ‖ CRAYON ‖
**When you finish, you will see something else that is fun to ride.**

Isabelle is helping her mother choose material to make a baby quilt.

**Can you find 8 Hidden Pictures® on the next page?** Answers on page 31

canoe

slice of pizza

heart

screwdriver

hot dog

ballet slipper

lollipop

tomato

# Scavenger Hunt

**Here are some more things to find:**

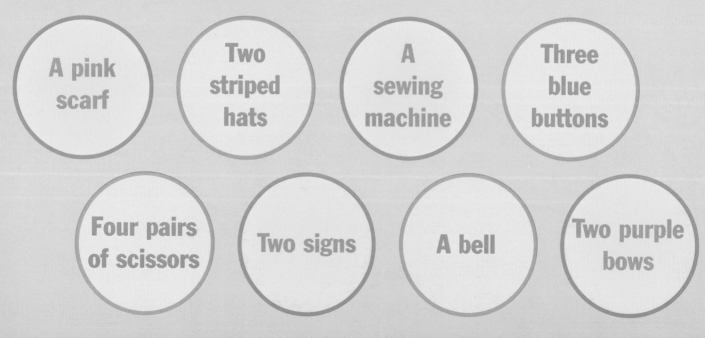

A pink scarf

Two striped hats

A sewing machine

Three blue buttons

Four pairs of scissors

Two signs

A bell

Two purple bows

**Can you find the Hidden Pictures below? When you finish, you can color in the**

rest of the scene.   CRAYON   Answers on page 31   Illustrated by Sally Springer

Tear out sticker sheet here.

451-CS-04

Hidden Pictures PLAYGROUND

Sydney and Cameron are watching the planes take off and land until it is time to leave for vacation.

**Can you find these items in the picture on the next page?**
**Be sure to find the right number of each.** Answers on page 31

**1** blue airplane

**2** dogs

**3** suitcases on wheels

**4** tickets

**5** hats

**6** hot dogs

It's fun to send postcards when you are on vacation. Draw a picture of a place you like to visit on this postcard. CRAYON

GREETINGS
from my favorite place

SNACK BAR

MENU

$4.00

# Moving Day

Justin and Jenna were moving to a new house. Dad drove the truck. Inside were most of Justin's and Jenna's toys and all the family's furniture. Justin and Jenna followed in the car with Mom.

"Will there be a basketball hoop at the new house?" Justin asked.

"I'm afraid not," Mom said. "We'll have to put one in."

"Until we do, I can help you practice," Jenna told her brother. "I'll chase you around the driveway while you dribble the basketball."

Justin grinned. "Thanks,"

A Hidden Pictures® Story by Erin Berger

he said.

"Will there be a swimming pool?" Jenna asked.

"No," Mom said, "but we can go to the community pool."

"I can walk you to the pool," Justin said. "You can wear your goggles, and I can use my watch to time you when you swim laps."

"Thanks," Jenna said. "I'm glad the new house will have one important thing."

"What's that?" Mom asked.

"Justin!" Jenna said with a laugh.

Justin laughed, too. "And I'm glad it will have Jenna!" he said.

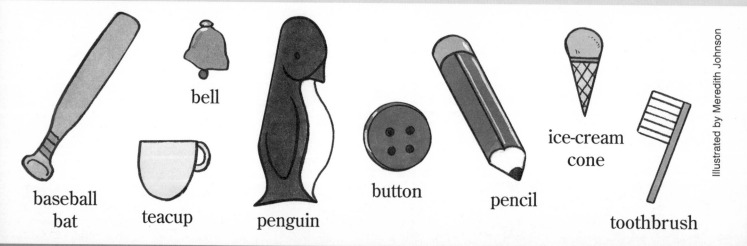

bell

baseball bat

teacup

penguin

button

pencil

ice-cream cone

toothbrush

Illustrated by Meredith Johnson

**After you finish the story, see if you can find these 8 Hidden Pictures in the scene.** Answers on page 32

rolling pin

dog bone

plate

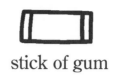
stick of gum

doughnut

tack

**Each object is hidden two times—once in each scene. We found and circled the tacks. Can you find the others?** Answers on page 32

**23**

 cookie  ring  snail  drinking glass  slice of fruit  barbell

**Can you find the Hidden Pictures below? When you finish, you can color in the**

Illustrated by Ellen Appleby

## Art Museum
## Pages 24–25

Place these stickers on the hidden objects as you find them.

book

acorn

sailboat

spool of thread

toothbrush

envelope

shoe

carrot

crescent
moon

ruler

whisk
broom

whale

**Highlights Hidden Pictures**
**PLAYGROUND**

Leo the artist is painting the flowers for sale
in this street-corner stall.

**Can you find these shapes in the picture on the next page?** Answers on page 32

Illustrated by Mike Moran

**What kinds of flowers do you like?**
**Draw them in this flower bed.** CRAYON

# Hidden Pictures®

Caleb caught a wave just right, and he's riding it all the way.

**There are 12 objects hidden in this picture. How many can you find?**

Answers on page 32

# Hidden Words

carrot

key

snake

heart

The names of the 12 objects
are hidden below. Some are across.
Others are up and down.
Find and circle each word.

envelope

| k | e | y | f | q | e | c | f |
|---|---|---|---|---|---|---|---|
| d | o | u | g | h | n | u | t |
| o | w | x | c | e | v | p | f |
| g | j | q | a | a | e | s | j |
| b | z | x | r | r | l | p | w |
| o | w | j | r | t | o | o | z |
| n | x | r | o | z | p | o | x |
| e | m | i | t | t | e | n | w |
| f | s | n | a | k | e | z | q |
| j | q | g | p | e | a | r | j |

pear

ring

mitten

doughnut

spoon

cup

Illustrated by Joyce John

# Answers

**30**

**Cover**

**Hidden Pictures® ABC pages 2–3**

**Silly Bath Time page 5**

**Digging for Clams pages 6–7**

I always wear a woolly coat.
And when you cannot sleep,
Just count me one by one each night
Because I am a **sheep**.

If you want to see the stars,
I'll take you on a trip.
Climb inside and we'll blast off.
I am a **rocket ship**.

People say I have nine lives.
Now why would they say that?
I like to purr and take long naps.
Did you guess that I'm a **cat**?

I'm handy when your feet are cold
And when you go for walks.
I keep your "piggies" nice and warm.
I am a pair of **socks**.

**Game of Tag pages 8–9**

## Egg Search pages 10–11

It's a chick !

## Scavenger Hunt

**A pink scarf**
It is hanging on the back wall.

**Two striped hats**
A woman is wearing one.
A woman on the cover of a book about hats is wearing the other.

**A sewing machine**
It is on a shelf behind Isabelle.

**Three blue buttons**
They are on a yellow rack.

**Four pairs of scissors**
A woman is using one pair.
Another pair is on the counter.
Two more pair are hanging on a yellow rack.

**Two signs**
"Learn to Sew" is next to the sewing box.
"Sale" is near the door.

## Fabric Shop pages 14–15

## Half Pipe pages 12–13

It's a go-cart !

**A bell**
It is hanging over the door.

**Two purple bows**
They are in Isabelle's hair.

## Dog Walkers pages 16–17

## At the Airport page 19

# Answers

## Moving Day **page 21**

## Double Hidden Pictures® **pages 22–23**

## Art Museum **pages 24–25**

## Find the Shapes **page 27**

## Hidden Pictures Hidden Words **pages 28–29**